- LAURA STORY -

GOD OF EVERY STORY

WWW.LAURASTORYMUSIC.COM
WWW.BRENTWOODBENSON.COM
WWW.FAIRTRADESERVICES.COM

in association with

M000110910

CONTENTS

There Is a Kingdom

Words and Music by
LAURA STORY and
JASON INGRAM

O Love of God

Words and Music by
LAURA STORY, IAN CRON
and CINDY MORGAN

I Can Just Be Me

Words and Music by
LAURA STORY and
JASON INGRAM

Moderately ♩ = 84

I've been do-ing all that I_____ can to hold it all___ to-geth-

-er, piece by___ piece._____

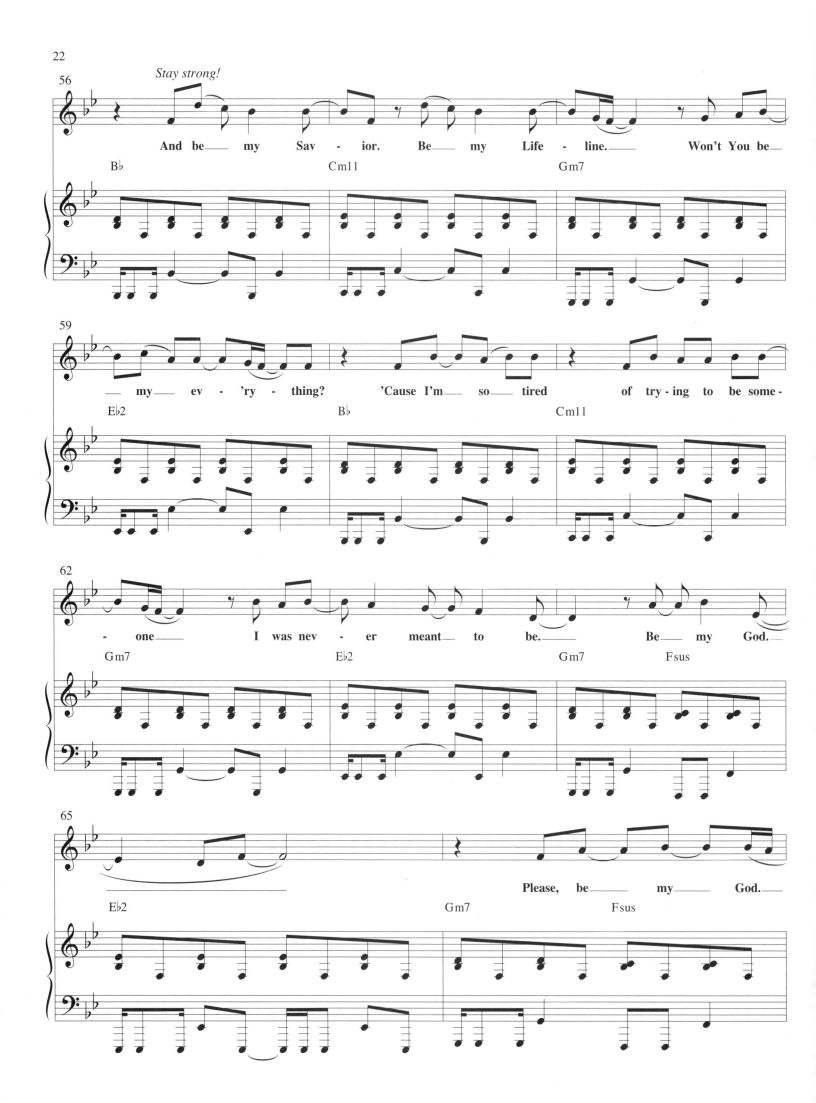

Who Is Like Our God?

Words and Music by
**LAURA STORY, ED CASH, FRANNI CASH,
JASON INGRAM and MATT MAHER**

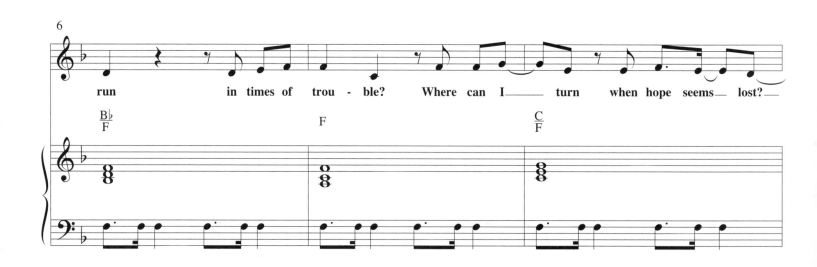

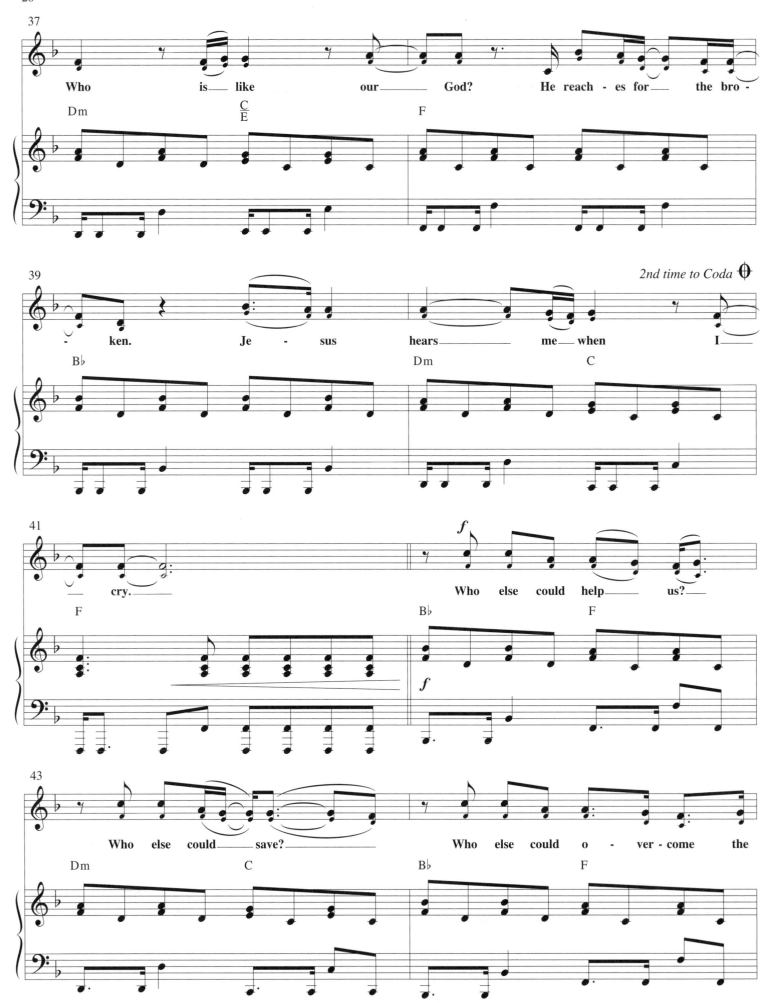

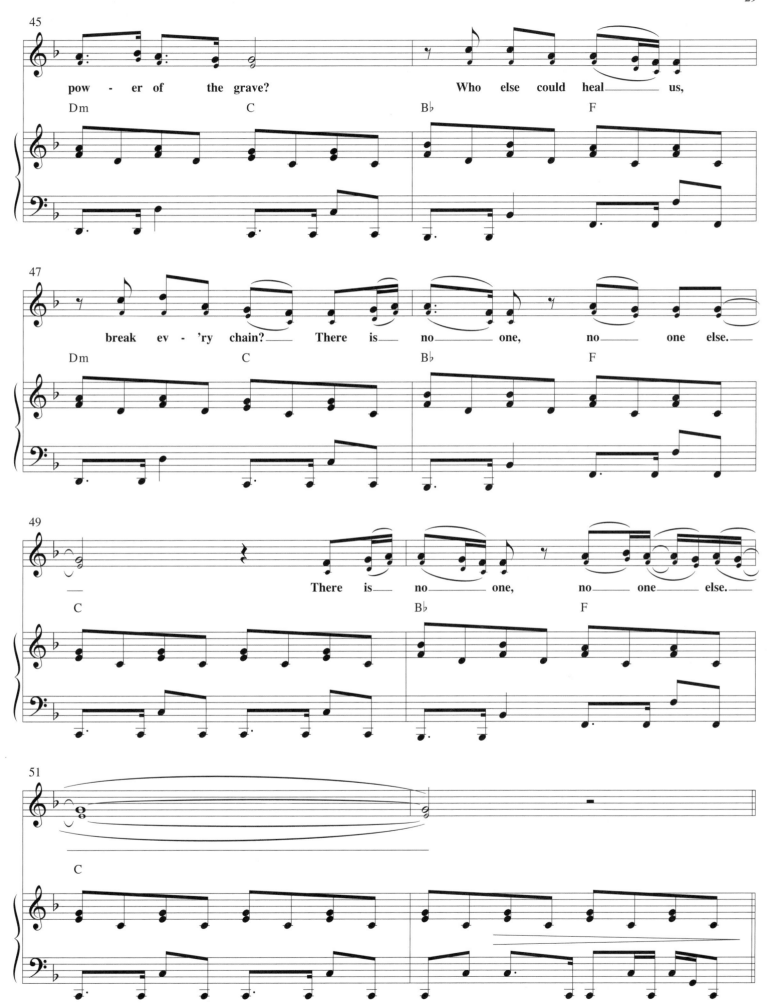

9
I find my strength with - in Your shel - ter. You will not
Gm/F
B♭/F
F
12
fail when the night is long.
C/F
B♭/F
15
mf
Who is like our God, might - y in the bat -
Dm
C/E
F
mf
17
- tle? Your maj - es - ty be lift - ed high.
B♭
Dm
C

God of Every Story

Words and Music by
LAURA STORY
and ED CASH

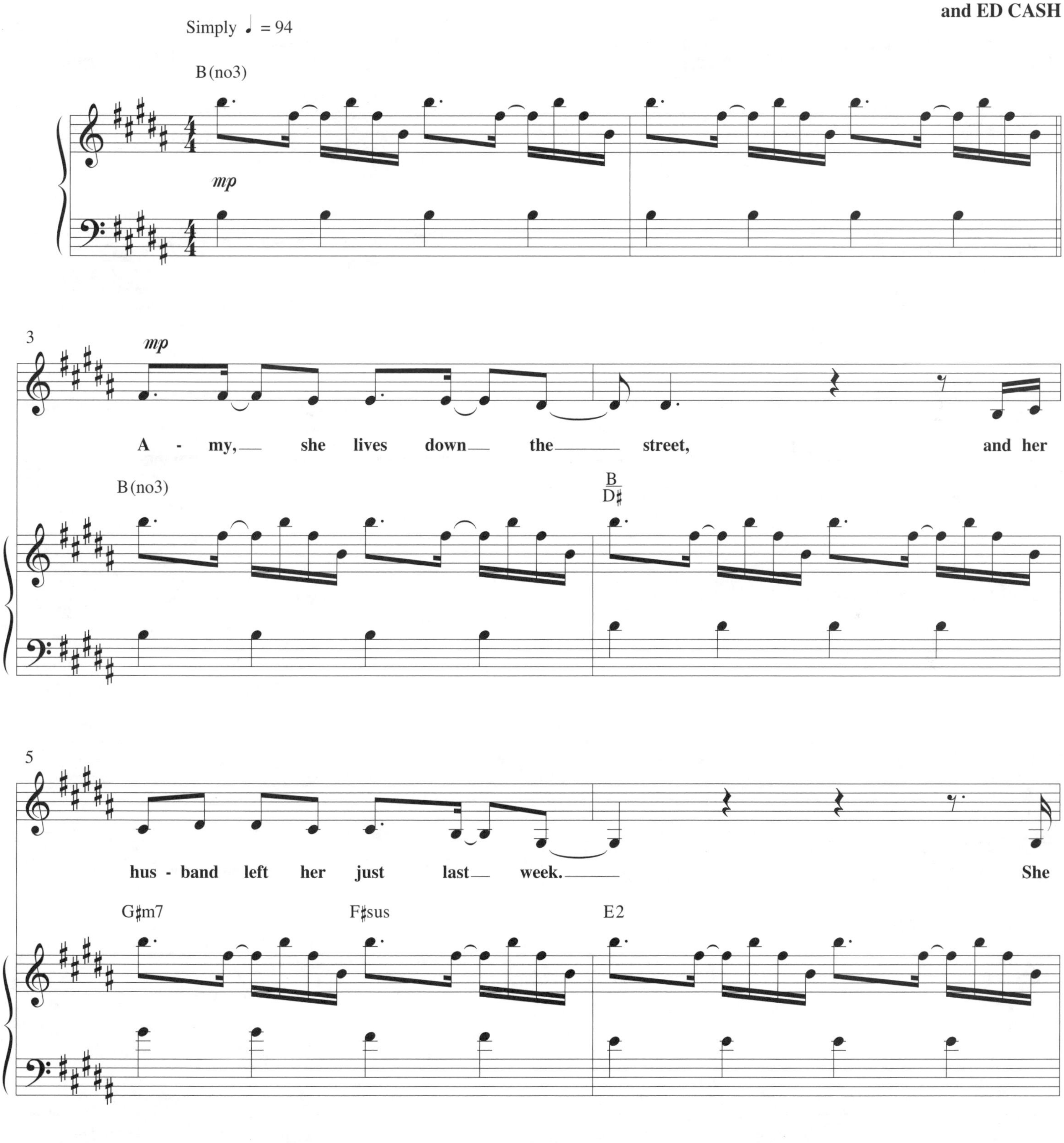

Simply ♩ = 94
B(no3)
mp
3
mp
A - my, she lives down the street, and her
B(no3)
B/D♯
5
hus - band left her just last week. She
G♯m7
F♯sus
E2

faith - ful. He's a faith - ful God.

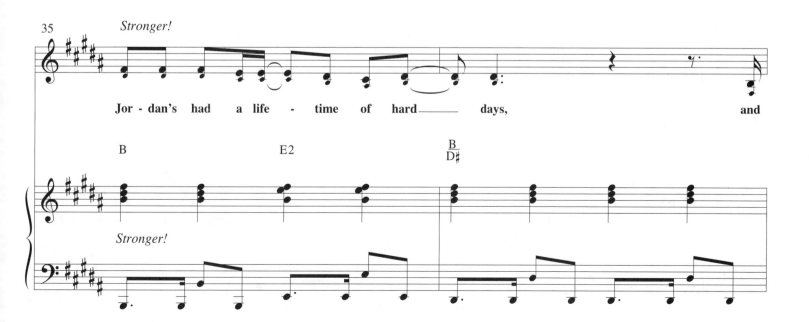

Stronger!

Jor - dan's had a life - time of hard days, and

Stronger!

Mar - tin____ is thank - ful____ he's____ a - live.____ The

doc - tors said he might not_____ sur - vive.____ That was

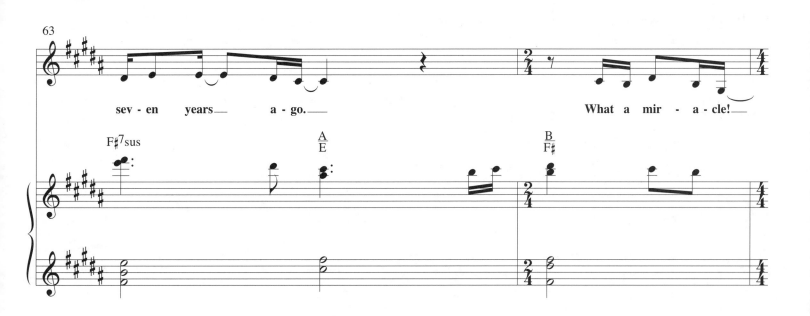

sev - en years____ a - go.____ What a mir - a - cle!____

Who But Jesus?

Words and Music by
LAURA STORY

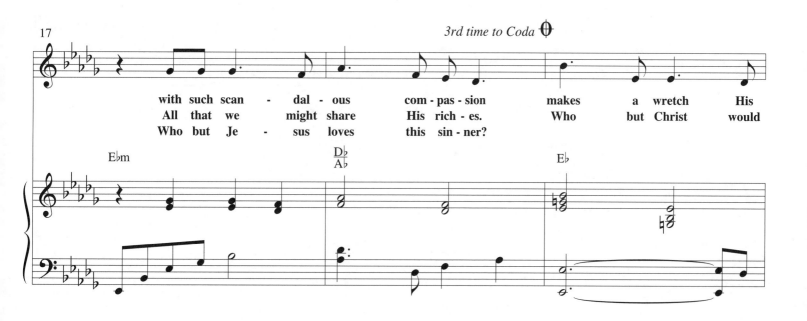

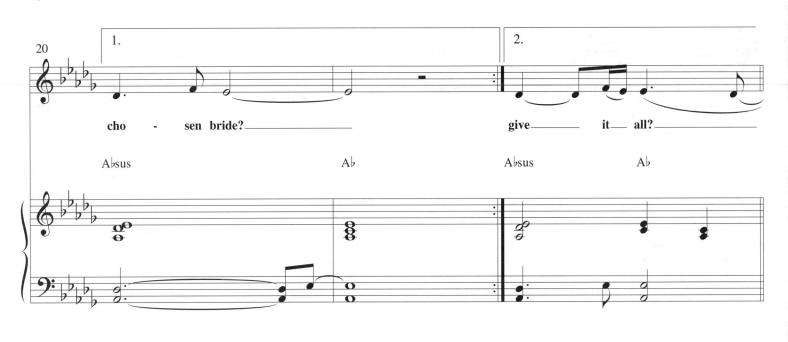

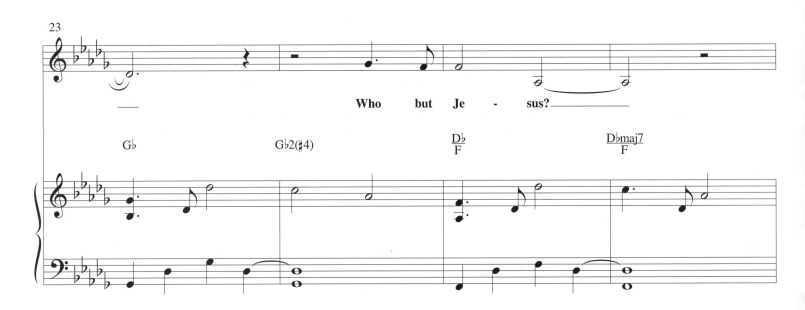

He a - lone is my right - eous - ness.

Eb   Absus   Ab   Gb

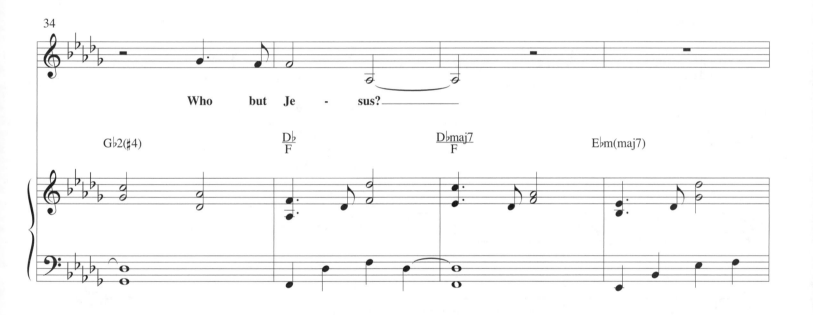

Who but Je - sus?

Gb2(#4)   Db/F   Dbmaj7/F   Ebm(maj7)

Who but Je - sus?

Ebm13   Absus   Ab   Absus

Keeper of the Stars

Words and Music by
LAURA STORY, JESS CATES
and ANTHONY SKINNER

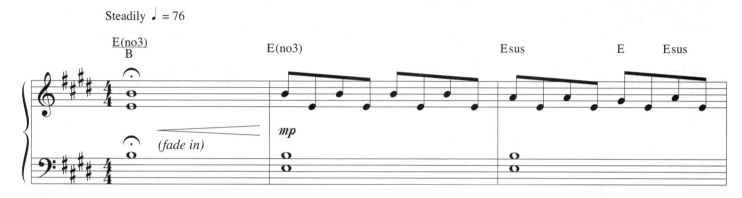

gainst all hope, in hope I be-lieve ____ that You, O Lord, ____ are faith-

58

D.S. al CODA 𝄋

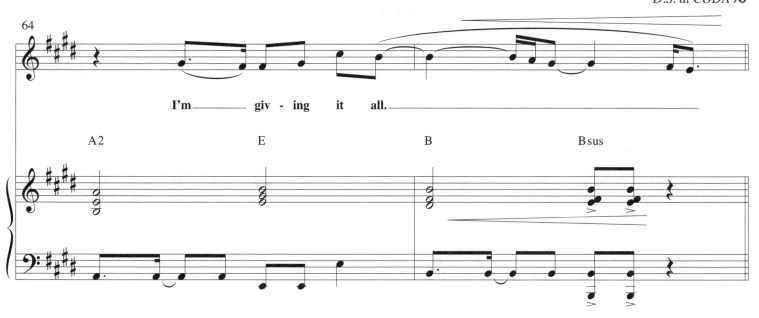

I'm_____ giv - ing it all._____

A2　　　　　E　　　　　B　　　　　Bsus

⊕ *CODA*

The Keep - er of the Stars.____

B　　　　　C♯m7　　B　　　A2　　　　　E

Bsus

Forgiven

Words and Music by
LAURA STORY, KERRIE ROBERTS
and ED CASH

Track begins with one measure percussion.

1. Do you re-mem-ber the last hand that was held out
(2.) -ber the last time you tru-ly

mp - mf a little less motion 1st time

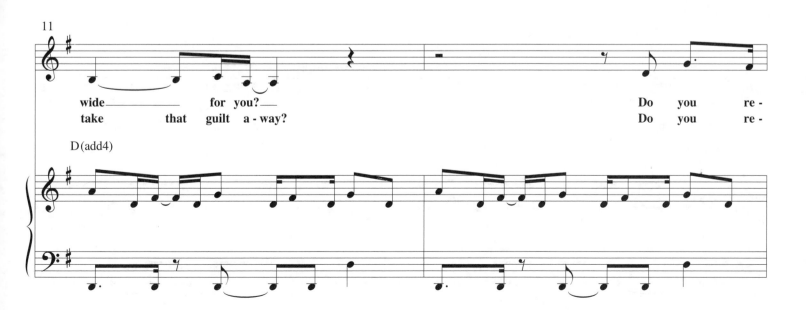

You Gave Your Life

Words and Music by
LAURA STORY

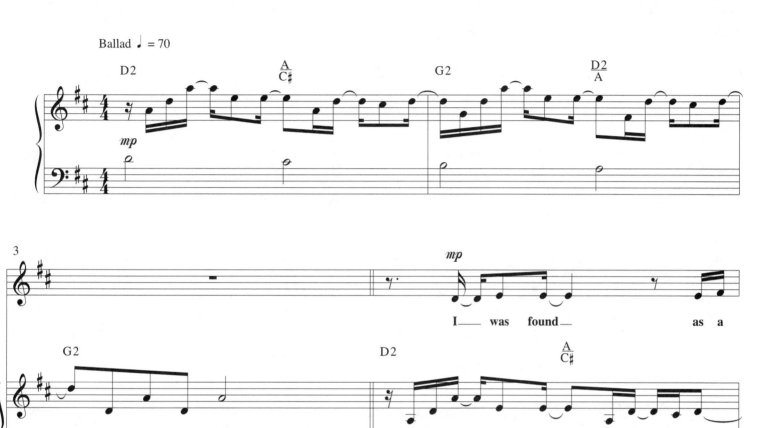

Grace

Words and Music by
LAURA STORY

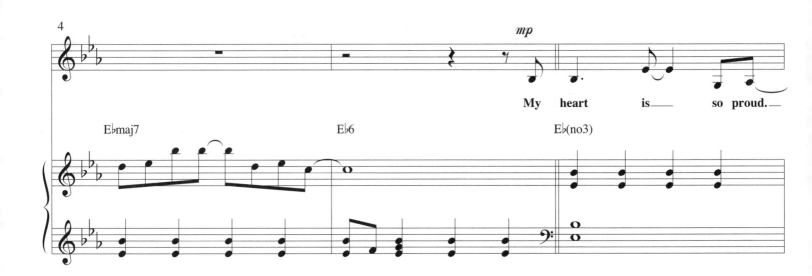

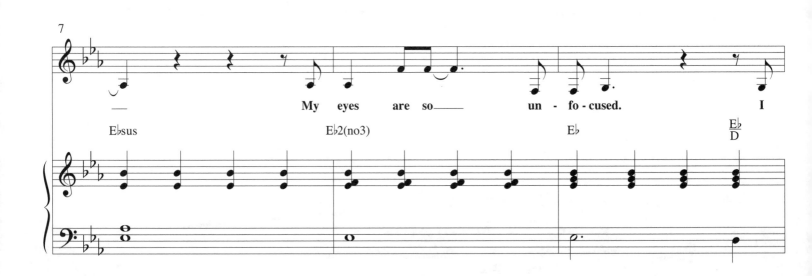

He Will Not Let Go

Words and Music by
LAURA STORY

There Is a Kingdom

**Words and Music by
LAURA STORY and
JASON INGRAM**

Key: F♯

F♯2
     There is a kingdom coming here tonight. There is a kingdom coming here tonight.
     B2/F♯   **F♯**
We're waiting, believing our God is alive.   There is a kingdom coming here tonight.

F♯2
     There is a stirring in this holy place. There is a stirring in this holy place.
     B2   **F♯2**
Your Spirit is urging our hearts to awake.   There is a stirring in this holy place.

          C♯sus   D♯m   **B2**   **C♯sus**
Church arise and sing for the joy, sing for the joy we've found!
          C♯sus   D♯m
With our lives, we shout out Your praise!
B2   **C♯sus   F♯2**
God, we proclaim Your kingdom's coming.

F♯2
     There is a fire starting in our souls. There is a fire starting in our souls.
   B2   **F♯2**
Reviving this longing, You're calling us home.   There is a fire starting in our souls.

B2   **C♯sus   B2**   **C♯sus**
     Every eye with expectation.   Every heart an invitation.
B2   **C♯sus   B2**   **C♯sus**
     Every eye with expectation.   Every heart an invitation.

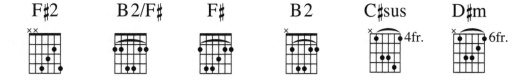

F♯2   B 2/F♯   F♯   B 2   C♯sus   D♯m

There Is a Kingdom

**Words and Music by
LAURA STORY and
JASON INGRAM**

Key: F♯ (Capo 2: E)

E2
  There is a kingdom coming here tonight. There is a kingdom coming here tonight.
  A2/E   **E**
We're waiting, believing our God is alive. There is a kingdom coming here tonight.

E2
  There is a stirring in this holy place. There is a stirring in this holy place.
  A2   **E2**
Your Spirit is urging our hearts to awake. There is a stirring in this holy place.

   Bsus **C♯m**   **A2**   **Bsus**
Church arise and sing for the joy, sing for the joy we've found!
   Bsus **C♯m**
With our lives, we shout out Your praise!
A2   **Bsus** **E2**
God, we proclaim Your kingdom's coming.

E2
  There is a fire starting in our souls. There is a fire starting in our souls.
  A2   **E2**
Reviving this longing, You're calling us home. There is a fire starting in our souls.

A2   **Bsus**   **A2**   **Bsus**
  Every eye with expectation. Every heart an invitation.
A2   **Bsus**   **A2**   **Bsus**
  Every eye with expectation. Every heart an invitation.

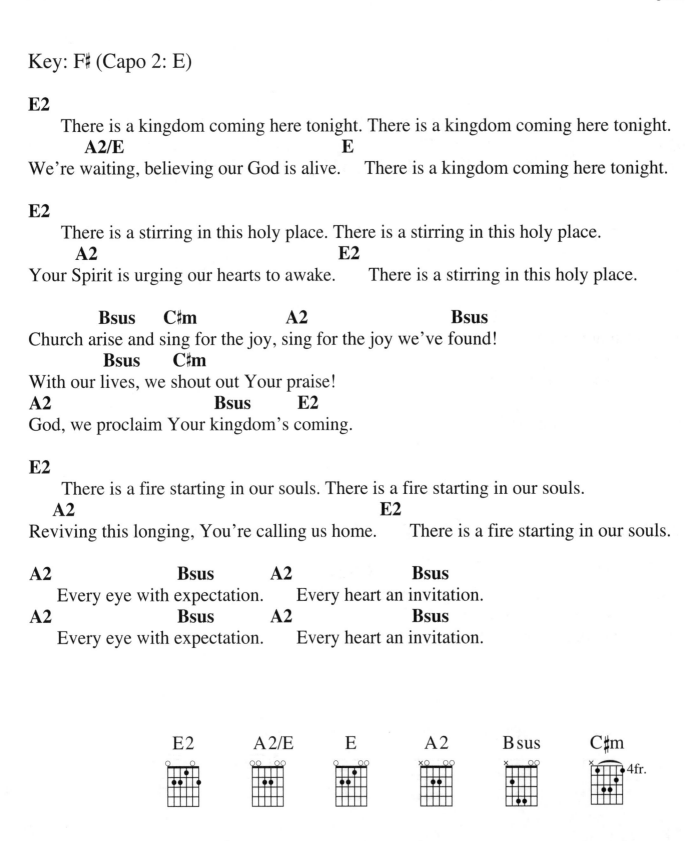

O Love of God

**Words and Music by
LAURA STORY, IAN CRON
and CINDY MORGAN**

Key: D

D G/D Bm/D A/D D G/D Bm/D A/D

      D G/D   Bm/D A/D   Bm   A/B   G2
O love of God,   strong and true,   in my barren soul, a river running through.
      D G/D   Bm/D   A/D   Bm   A/B G2
O love of God,   swift and straight,   You have washed away my sin and leave no trace.
Em7   G
    River, rise and carry me away.

  D/F♯   G   D/F♯   G
I see You in the stars above. I feel You in the earth below,
  Bm7   A
In waves that swell, in winds that blow.
  D/F♯   G   D/F♯   G   Bm7
I marvel at the mystery that One so great could love someone like me,
        A   D G/D Bm/D A/D   D G/D Bm/D A/D
Undeserved and free. O love of God!   O love of God!

      D G   Bm A   Bm   A/B G2
O love of God,   wondrous to me   that this quivering soul was lost and found in Thee.
      D G   Bm A   Bm   A/B G2   D
O love of God,   my Shield and Stay,   will You turn me to the oceans of   Your grace?
Em7   G
    River, rise and carry me away.

D	G/D	Bm/D	A/D	Bm	A/B

G2	Em7	G	D/F♯	Bm7	A

I Can Just Be Me

**Words and Music by
LAURA STORY and
JASON INGRAM**

Key: B♭

B♭   B♭/C   Gm7   B♭/E♭

B♭   B♭/A   Gm7   E♭2
I've been doing all that I can to hold it all together, piece by piece.
B♭   B♭/A   Gm7   E♭2
I've been feeling like a failure, trying to be braver than I could ever be.
           Cm11
It's just not me.

B♭   Cm11   Gm7   E♭2
   So, be my Healer. Be my Comfort. Be my peace.
B♭   Cm11   Gm7   E♭2   Gm7   Fsus   E♭2
   'Cause I can be broken. I can be needy. Lord, I need You now to be,   be my God,
                        B♭   B♭/A   Gm7   B♭/E♭
So I can just be me.

B♭   B♭/A   Gm7   E♭2
I've been living like an orphan, trying to belong here, but it's just not my home.
B♭   B♭/A   Gm7   E♭2
I've been holding on so tightly to all the things that I think can satisfy my soul,
           Cm11
But I'm letting   go.

B♭   **Cm11**   **Gm7**   **E♭2**
So be my Father, my mighty Warrior. Be my King.
B♭   **Cm11**   **Gm7**   **E♭2**   **Gm7**
'Cause I can be scattered, frail and shattered. Lord, I need You now to be,
Fsus **E♭2**
Be my God, so I can just be me.

Gm7   **Fsus**   **E♭2**   **Gm7** **Fsus**   **E♭2**
'Cause I was lost   in this dark world   till I was finally found in You.
B♭/D   **E♭2**   **Gm7** **Fsus**   **F(add4)/A**
So now, I'm needing, desperately pleading,   O Lord,   be all to me.

B♭   **Cm11**   **Gm7**   **E♭2**
And be my Savior. Be my Lifeline. Won't You be my everything?
B♭   **Cm11**   **Gm7**   **E♭2**   **Gm7**
'Cause I'm so tired   of trying to be someone I was never meant to be.
Fsus **E♭2** **Gm7**   **Fsus** **E♭2** **Gm7** **Fsus** **E♭**
Be my God.   Please, be my God.   Be my God,
          B♭ **B♭/A**   **Gm7** **B♭/E♭**
So I can just be me,   so I can just be me,   I can just be me.

I Can Just Be Me

Words and Music by
LAURA STORY and
JASON INGRAM

Key: B♭ (Capo 3: G)

G   G/A   Em7   G/C

G   **G/F♯**   **Em7**   **C2**
I've been doing all that I can to hold it all together, piece by piece.
G   **G/F♯**   **Em7**   **C2**
I've been feeling like a failure, trying to be braver than I could ever be.
                Am11
It's just not me.

G   **Am11**   **Em7**   **C2**
   So, be my Healer. Be my Comfort. Be my peace.
G   **Am11**   **Em7**   **C2**   **Em7   Dsus   C2**
   'Cause I can be broken. I can be needy. Lord, I need You now to be,   be my God,
                G   G/F♯   Em7   G/C
So I can just be me.

G   **G/F♯**   **Em7**   **C2**
I've been living like an orphan, trying to belong here, but it's just not my home.
G   **G/F♯**   **Em7**   **C2**
I've been holding on so tightly to all the things that I think can satisfy my soul,
                Am11
But I'm letting   go.

G   G/A   Em7   G/C   G/F♯

C2   Am11   Dsus   G/B   D(add4)/F♯

G   Am11   Em7   C2
So be my Father, my mighty Warrior. Be my King.
G   Am11   Em7   C2   Em7
'Cause I can be scattered, frail and shattered. Lord, I need You now to be,
Dsus C2
Be my God, so I can just be me.

Em7   Dsus   C2   Em7 Dsus   C2
'Cause I was lost   in this dark world   till I was finally found in You.
G/B   C2   Em7 Dsus   D(add4)/F♯
So now, I'm needing, desperately pleading,   O Lord,   be all to me.

G   Am11   Em7   C2
And be my Savior. Be my Lifeline. Won't You be my everything?
G   Am11   Em7   C2   Em7
'Cause I'm so tired   of trying to be someone I was never meant to be.
Dsus C2 Em7   Dsus C2 Em7 Dsus C
Be my God.   Please, be my God.   Be my God,
        G G/F♯   Em7 G/C
So I can just be me,   so I can just be me,   I can just be me.

Who Is Like Our God?

Words and Music by
LAURA STORY, ED CASH, FRANNI CASH,
JASON INGRAM and MATT MAHER

Key: F

F(no3)

      Bb/F   **F**   **C/F**   **Gm/F**
Where can I run in times of trouble? Where can I turn when hope seems lost?
      Bb/F   **F**   **C/F**   **Bb/F**
I find my strength within Your shelter. You will not fail when the night is long.

Dm   **C/E**   **F**   **Bb**   **Dm**   **C**
Who is like   our God, mighty in the battle? Your majesty be lifted high.
Dm   **C/E**   **F**   **Bb**   **Dm**   **C**   **F**
Who is like   our God? He reaches for the broken. Jesus hears me when I cry.

      Bb   **F**   **C**   **Gm**
How can it be that You are for me? Though I am weak, Your love is strong.
      Bb   **F**   **C**   **Gm**
You are my Light and my Salvation. In Your name alone I overcome.

Bb   **F**   **Dm**   **C**
   Who else could help us?   Who else could save?
Bb   **F**   **Dm**   **C**
   Who else could overcome the power of the grave?
Bb   **F**   **Dm**   **C**
   Who else could heal us,   break every chain?
      Bb **F**   **C**   **Bb** **F**   **C**
There is no one, no one else. There is no one, no one else.

      Bb2   **Dm**
He hears me when I cry. He hears me when I cry. Oh!
   Bb2   **F** **F4(2)** **F**
Who is like, who is like our God?

F(no3)   Bb/F   F   C/F   Gm/F   Dm

C/E   Bb   C   Gm   Bb2   F2

Who Is Like Our God?

Words and Music by
**LAURA STORY, ED CASH, FRANNI CASH,
JASON INGRAM and MATT MAHER**

Key: F (Capo 3: D)

D(no3)

      G/D   **D**   **A/D**   **Em/D**
Where can I run in times of trouble? Where can I turn when hope seems lost?
      G/F   **D**   **A/D**   **G/D**
I find my strength within Your shelter. You will not fail when the night is long.

Bm **A/C♯** **D**   **G**   **Bm** **A**
Who is like   our God, mighty in the battle? Your majesty be lifted high.
Bm **A/C♯** **D**   **G**   **Bm** **A** **D**
Who is like   our God? He reaches for the broken. Jesus hears me when I cry.

      G   **D**   **A**   **Em**
How can it be that You are for me? Though I am weak, Your love is strong.
      G   **D**   **A**   **Em**
You are my Light and my Salvation. In Your name alone I overcome.

G   **D** **Bm**   **A**
Who else could help us?   Who else could save?
G   **D** **Bm**   **A**
Who else could overcome the power of the grave?
G   **D** **Bm**   **A**
Who else could heal us,   break every chain?
      G **D** **A** **G** **D** **A**
There is no one, no one else. There is no one, no one else.

      G2   **Bm**
He hears me when I cry. He hears me when I cry. Oh!
  G2   **D** **D4(2)** **D**
Who is like, who is like our God?

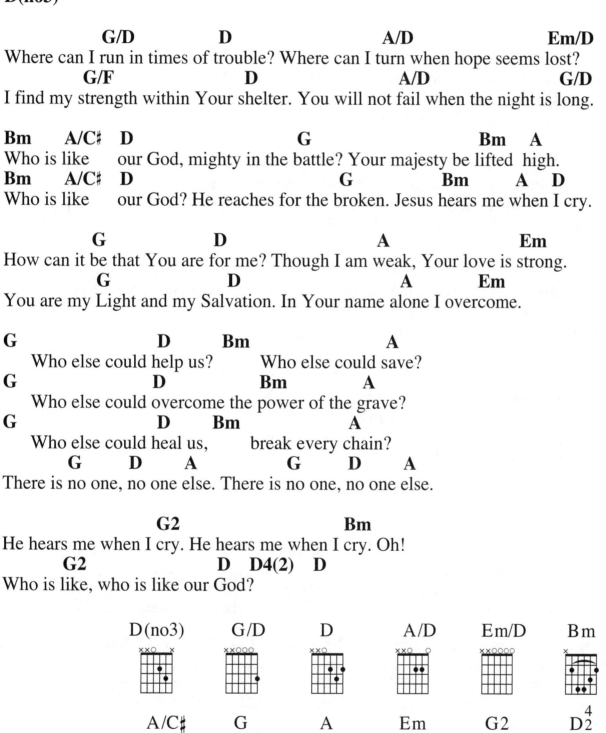

God of Every Story

Words and Music by
LAURA STORY
and ED CASH

Key: B

B(no3)

B(no3)   **B/D♯**   **G♯m7**   **F♯sus**   **E2**
Amy, she lives down the street, and her husband left her just last week.
    E2   **F♯sus**   **B/D♯**   **E2**
She feels like giving up, but she's holding on to hope.

B(no3)   **B/D♯**   **G♯m7**   **F♯sus**   **E2**
John lost his job six months ago. He's got a wife, three kids at home.
    E2   **F♯sus**   **B/D♯**   **E2**
Doesn't know what to do. He's praying for a breakthrough.

C♯m11   **G♯m7**   **C♯m11**   **G♯m7**
Some want to raise a fist up high and blame all the hard things on the Father in the sky,
   E2   **F♯sus**   **B/D♯**   **E2**
But He hears when we call, and we can trust Him through it all.

    B/D♯   **E2**   **F♯sus**   **F♯**   **B/D♯**   **E2**   **F♯sus**   **F♯**
He is the God of every story.   He sees each tear that falls.
    B/D♯   **E2**   **F♯sus**   **G♯m7**   **E2**
You may not understand, but one thing is certain: He is faithful.
    F♯sus   **F♯**   **B(no3)**
He's a faithful   God.

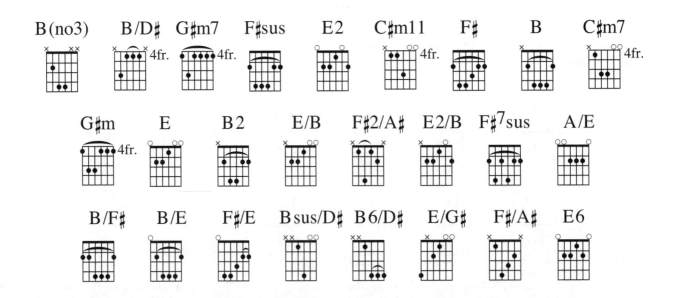

B   E2   B/D♯   G♯m7   F♯   E2

Jordan's had a lifetime of hard days, and all the pills won't take the pain away.

      E2   F♯   B/D♯   E2

But before he hits the ground, He sees mercy reaching down.

          B   E2   F♯sus F♯   B   E2   F♯sus F♯

He is the God of every story.   He sees each tear that falls.

  B/D♯   E2   F♯sus   G♯m7   E2

We may not understand, but one thing is certain: He is faithful.

     F♯sus F♯

He's a faithful   God.

C♯m7   B/D♯   G♯m   F♯sus

    His ways are higher   than we could ever comprehend.

C♯m7   B/D♯   G♯m   F♯sus F♯

    When our world is shaken, He holds us in the palm of His hand.

    B(no3) E   B2   E/B   F♯2/A♯   E2/B

And Martin is thankful he's alive. The doctors said he might not survive.

     F♯7sus   A/E   B/F♯   F♯7sus

That was seven years ago.   What a miracle!

  B/D♯   E2   B/D♯ B

And now there's this new baby girl,

  G♯m7   F♯   B/F♯   E   B/E F♯/E E

And with one breath she's changed our whole world.

    E   F♯sus   Bsus/D♯ B/D♯ B6/D♯ B/D♯   E B/E F♯sus F♯

Some say she looks like dad, but she looks   like   grace   to me,

    E/G♯   F♯/A♯

Your grace to me.

         B   E2   F♯sus F♯   B   E2   F♯sus F♯

You're the God of every story.   You've seen each tear that falls.

  B/D♯   E2   F♯sus   G♯m7   E2   F♯sus F♯

We may not understand, but one thing is certain: You are faithful. You are faithful.

        B   E2/B F♯sus F♯   B   E2/B   F♯sus F♯

You're the God of every   story,   no matter what I'm going through.

  B/D♯   E6 E F♯sus   G♯m7   E F♯/E E2

I may not understand.   You are God, and I am just a man.

    F♯sus   G♯m7   E F♯/E E2

Yeah, I'm forever trusting in Your plan.

F♯sus   G♯m7   E2   F♯sus F♯ B

One thing is certain: You are faithful. You're a faith-   ful God.

God of Every Story

Words and Music by
LAURA STORY
and ED CASH

Key: B (Capo 2: A)

A(no3)

A(no3)   **A/C♯**   **F♯m7**   **Esus**   **D2**
Amy, she lives down the street, and her husband left her just last week.
  D2   **Esus**   **A/C♯**   **D2**
She feels like giving up, but she's holding on to hope.

A(no3)   **A/C♯**   **F♯m7**   **Esus**   **D2**
John lost his job six months ago. He's got a wife, three kids at home.
  D2   **Esus**   **A/C♯**   **D2**
Doesn't know what to do. He's praying for a breakthrough.

Bm11   **F♯m7**   **Bm11**   **F♯m7**
Some want to raise a fist up high and blame all the hard things on the Father in the sky,
  D2   **Esus**   **A/C♯**   **D2**
But He hears when we call, and we can trust Him through it all.

   A/C♯   **D2**   **Esus**   **E**   **A/C♯**   **D2**   **Esus**   **E**
He is the God of every story.   He sees each tear that falls.
   A/C♯   **D2**   **Esus**   **F♯m7**   **D2**
You may not understand, but one thing is certain: He is faithful.
   Esus   **E**   **A(no3)**
He's a faithful   God.

A(no3)   A/C♯   F♯m7   Esus   D2   Bm11   E   A   Bm7

F♯m   D   A2   D/A   E2/G♯   D2/A   E7sus   G/D

A/E   A/D   E/D   Asus/C♯   A6/C♯   D/F♯   E/G♯   D6

A   D2   A/C♯   F♯m7   E   D2
Jordan's had a lifetime of hard days, and all the pills won't take the pain away.
  D2   E   A/C♯   D2
But before he hits the ground, He sees mercy reaching down.

    A D2 Esus E A   D2 Esus E
He is the God of every story.   He sees each tear that falls.
  A/C♯   D2   Esus F♯m7   D2
We may not understand, but one thing is certain: He is faithful.
   Esus E
He's a faithful God.

Bm7   A/C♯ F♯m   Esus
  His ways are higher   than we could ever comprehend.
Bm7   A/C♯   F♯m Esus E
  When our world is shaken, He holds us in the palm of His hand.

  A(no3) D   A2   D/A   E2/G♯   D2/A
And Martin is thankful he's alive. The doctors said he might not survive.
   E7sus   G/D A/E   E7sus
That was seven years ago.   What a miracle!

  A/C♯   D2   A/C♯ A
And now there's this new baby girl,
 F♯m7   E   A/E   D   A/D E/D D
And with one breath she's changed our whole world.
   D   Esus   Asus/C♯ A/C♯ A6/C♯ A/C♯ D A/D Esus E
Some say she looks like dad, but she looks   like grace   to me,
   D/F♯   E/G♯
Your grace to me.

    A   D2 Esus E   A   D2   Esus E
You're the God of every story.   You've seen each tear that falls.
  A/C♯   D2   Esus F♯m7   D2   Esus E
We may not understand, but one thing is certain: You are faithful. You are faithful.
    A D2/A Esus E   A   D2/A Esus E
You're the God of every story,   no matter what I'm going through.
 A/C♯   D6 D Esus   F♯m7   D E/D D2
I may not understand.   You are God, and I am just a man.
   Esus   F♯m7   D E/D D2
Yeah, I'm forever trusting in Your plan.
Esus   F♯m7   D2   Esus D A
One thing is certain: You are faithful. You're a faith- ful God.

Who But Jesus?

Words and Music by
LAURA STORY

Key: D♭

D♭   A♭/C   E♭m11   D♭   D♭2   B♭m7   G♭   G♭2   G♭

D♭   A♭/C E♭m11   D♭   A♭/C   B♭m7   G♭   G♭2   G♭
Who but Jesus   loves   the   sin-   ner?   Who but Jesus calls him friend,
D♭   A♭/C E♭m11   D♭   A♭/C   B♭m7   G♭   G♭2   G♭
Reaches out to   touch   the   lep-   er,   bids the weary come to Him?
E♭m   B♭   B♭7sus   E♭m   B♭   A♭sus   A♭
Who but Jesus loves the lonely,   those the world has cast aside,
E♭m   D♭/A♭   E♭   A♭sus   A♭
With such scandalous compassion makes a wretch His chosen bride?

D♭   A♭/C E♭m11   D♭   A♭/C   B♭m7   G♭   G♭2   G♭
Who but Jesus   dwelt   a- mong us,   called this broken world His home,
D♭   A♭/C E♭m11   D♭   A♭/C   B♭m7   G♭   G♭2   G♭
Took on flesh and   pain   and sor-   row,   reaping what He did not sow?
E♭m   B♭   B♭7sus   E♭m   B♭   A♭sus   A♭
With the lost, He shared salvation.   With the thief, He shared a cross.
E♭m   D♭/A♭   E♭   A♭sus   A♭
All that we might share His riches. Who but Christ would give it all?

G♭   G♭2(♯4)   D♭/F   D♭maj7/F   E♭m(maj7)   E♭m13   A♭sus   A♭
Who but Jesus?   Who but Jesus?

D♭   A♭/C E♭m11   D♭   A♭/C   B♭m7   G♭   G♭2   G♭
Who but Jesus   loves   the   sin-   ner   enough to give His life?
D♭   A♭/C E♭m11   D♭   A♭/C   B♭m7   G♭   G♭2   G♭
Love too pure for   man   to   mer-   it,   grace too glorious to   deny.
E♭m   B♭   B♭7sus   E♭m   B♭   A♭sus   A♭
Praise Him now, my joy in living.   Yes, in death my comfort rests.
E♭m   D♭/A♭   E♭   A♭sus   A♭
Who but Jesus loves this sinner? He alone is my righteousness.

D♭   A♭/C   E♭m11   D♭2   B♭m7   G♭   G♭2   E♭m   B♭

B♭7sus   A♭sus   A♭   D♭/A♭   G♭2(♯4)   D♭/F   D♭maj7/F   E♭m(maj7)   E♭m13

Who But Jesus?

Words and Music by
LAURA STORY

Key: Db (Capo 1: C)

C   G/B   Dm11   C   C2   Am7   F   F2   F

C   G/B   Dm11   C   G/B   Am7   F   F2   F
Who but Jesus   loves   the   sin- ner?   Who but Jesus calls him friend,
C   G/B   Dm11   C   G/B   Am7   F   F2   F
Reaches out to   touch   the   lep- er,   bids the weary come to Him?
Dm   A   A7sus   Dm   A   Gsus   G
Who but Jesus loves the lonely,   those the world has cast aside,
Dm   C/G   D   Gsus   G
With such scandalous compassion makes a wretch His chosen bride?

C   G/B   Dm11   C   G/B   Am7   F   F2   F
Who but Jesus   dwelt   a- mong us,   called this broken world His home,
C   G/B   Dm11   C   G/B   Am7   F   F2   F
Took on flesh and   pain   and sor- row,   reaping what He did not sow?
Dm   A   A7sus   Dm   A   Gsus   G
With the lost, He shared salvation.   With the thief, He shared a cross.
Dm   C/G   D   Gsus   G
All that we might share His riches. Who but Christ would give it all?

F   F2(♯4)   C/E   Cmaj7/E   Dm(maj7)   Dm13   Gsus   G
   Who but Jesus?   Who but Jesus?

C   G/B   Dm11   C   G/B   Am7   F   F2   F
Who but Jesus   loves   the   sin- ner   enough to give His life?
C   G/B   Dm11   C   G/B   Am7   F   F2   F
Love too pure for   man   to   mer- it,   grace too glorious to deny.
Dm   A   A7sus   Dm   A   Gsus   G
Praise Him now, my joy in living.   Yes, in death my comfort rests.
Dm   C/G   D   Gsus   G
Who but Jesus loves this sinner? He alone is my righteousness.

C   G/B   Dm11   C2   Am7   F   F2   Dm   A

A7sus   Gsus   G   C/G   F2(♯4)   C/E   Cmaj7/E   Dm(maj7)   Dm13

Keeper of the Stars

Words and Music by
LAURA STORY, JESS CATES
and ANTHONY SKINNER

Key: E

E(no3)/B   E(no3)   Esus   E   Esus   E(no3)   A2/C♯

E(no3)   **Esus**   **E**   **Esus**   **E(no3)**
Against all hope, in hope I believe that You, O Lord, are faithful.
                 A/C♯   **C♯m**   **A/C♯**
You're good, and You are able.
E(no3)   **Esus**   **E**   **Esus**   **E(no3)**
When it seems impossible to me, Your promises are all true.
             A   **Amaj7**   **A**
What You say, I know You will do.
  F♯m **C♯m**   **B**   **Bsus** **B**   **F♯m** **C♯m**   **B**
And I   am sure   Your love   endures.

A2   **E**   **B**   **C♯m7** **B**
   I'm giving it all to the Keeper of the Stars.
A2 **E**   **B**   **C♯m7** **B**
   I won't be afraid, 'cause You're holding every part
A2   **E**   **B**   **C♯m7**   **B**
   Of this world,   of my heart. Trusting that You won't let me fall,
A2   **E**   **B**
   I'm giving it all to the Keeper of the Stars.

A2 **E** **B** **C♯m7** **B** **A2** **E** **B**

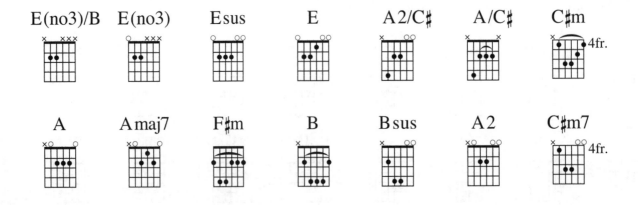

<pre>
E(no3)   Esus   E   Esus E(no3)
Against all hope, in hope I believe Your plan for me is   perfect,
                          A/C♯   C♯m   A/C♯
And You show me it's all worth it.
      E(no3)   Esus   E   Esus E(no3)
With eyes of faith, You teach me to see the light in every   dark night,
           A/C♯   Amaj7   A
Knowing it will   be alright.
    F♯m C♯m   B Bsus   B   F♯m C♯m   B
And I   am sure   that   Your love   endures, yeah!

A2   E   B   C♯m7   B
   I'm giving it all to the Keeper of the Stars.
A2   E   B   C♯m7   B
   I won't be afraid, 'cause You're holding every part
A2   E   B   C♯m7   B
   Of this world,   of my heart. Trusting that You won't let me fall,
A2   E   B   C♯m7   B
   I'm giving it all to the Keeper of the Stars.
A2   E   B   C♯m7   B   A2   E   B
        You're the Keeper of the Stars.

C♯m7   E   A2   B   Bsus
   Look up now, O my soul;   see His greatness and behold, behold.
C♯m7   E   A2   B   Bsus
   Look up now, O my soul;   see His wonders and behold, behold.
A2   E   B C♯m7 Bsus A2   E   B   Bsus
   I'm giving it all.   I'm giving it all.

   C♯m7 B   A2   E   Bsus
The Keeper of the Stars.
</pre>

Forgiven

**Words and Music by
LAURA STORY, KERRIE ROBERTS
and ED CASH**

Key: G

Gmaj7

      Gmaj7   **Em9**
Do you remember the last hand that was held out   to you,
    Em9   **A7sus**
The last time you heard the words inviting you to come,
   A7sus   **D(add4)**
The last time there were arms open wide for you?
      C2(♯4)   **Gmaj7/B**
Do you remember ever knowing anyone
     A7sus   **D(add4)**
Who saw you as someone, who called you by name?

       Gmaj7   **Em9**
And said, "Forgiven, every word and deed. You are forgiven."
  Em9   **Am7** **G/B**   **C2**
He says to you, "My child, you are chosen. You are loved.
    D(add4)   **Gmaj7**
You are   forgiven."

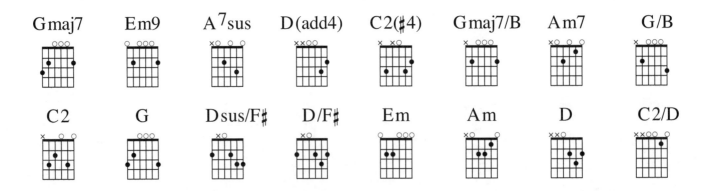

Gmaj7   **Em9**
Do you remember the last time you truly   felt safe,
    Em9   **A7sus**
The last time you were honest about your fear and pain,
A7sus   **D(add4)**
Knowing there was someone who could take that guilt away?
    C2(♯4)   **Gmaj7/B**
Do you remember when you heard those words of love,
   A7sus   **D(add4)**
Believing in your heart that you were worth the cost?

      Gmaj7   **Em9**
"You are forgiven, every word and deed. You are forgiven."
   Em9   **Am7** **G/B**   **C2**
He says to you, "My child, you are chosen. You are loved.
    D(add4)   **C2(♯4)**   **C2**
You are   forgiven."

G   **Dsus/F♯** **D/F♯** **Em**   **C2**
I am set   free.   All my stains are washed clean.
G   **Dsus/F♯** **D/F♯** **Em**   **C2**
Jesus, my God and King, thank You for saving me.

      Gmaj7   **Em9**   **Am**   **G/B**   **C2**
I am forgiven. I am   forgiven. I am chosen. I am loved.

  D   **Gmaj7**   **Em9**
I am forgiven. I have been set free. I've been forgiven.
Em9   **Am7**   **G/B**   **C2**   **C2/D**
Say to me, "My child, you are chosen. You are loved."
      Am7 **G/B** **C2**   **Gmaj7**   **C2(♯4)**
And that will always be   enough. I am   forgiven.

You Gave Your Life

**Words and Music by
LAURA STORY**

Key: D

D2   A/C♯   G2   D2/A   G2

D2   **A/C♯**   **G2**   **D2/A**   **G2   D/A**   **Asus   A**
    I was found as a beggar, as an orphan with no home   and no family.
D2   **A/C♯**   **G/B**   **D2/A**   **G2**
    I was found with a stain as deep as darkness fills the night.
       Em   **Dsus**   **D**   **A(add4)/C♯**   **D**
But the wonder does not lie in the depression of my state,
          C   **G/B**   **D/A   D2/A   D/A   Asus   A**
But that You found me at all is simply grace   upon   grace.

D   **G2**   **Bm**   **D/A**   **Gmaj7   A**
    You gave Your life for me,   for this wandering soul to   see
    G   **D/F♯**   **F♯**   **G/B   A   G   A   D2**
How far, how wide, how deep, how high is the relentless love of God.

D2   **A/C♯**   **G2**   **D2/A**   **G2**
    And now I find that the comforts of this heart are not in things
    D/A   **Asus   A**
Or in the joys that this life brings,
D2   **A/C♯**   **G2**   **D2/A**   **G2**   **A(add4)**   **A**
    But just to be the very workmanship of God, to know He's with me, to know He's for me.
    Em   **Dsus   D**   **A(add4)/C♯**   **D**
And I can't begin to comprehend just why He's chosen me,
    C   **G/B**   **D/A   D2/A   D/A   Asus**   **A**
But I'd spend a thousand lifetimes giving thanks,   giving You thanks.

G2   **D/F♯   G2**   **D/F♯**
    I am undeserving   of grace so amazing.
G2   **D/F♯**   **G2   Asus   A**
    Though free to me, it cost You everything.

D2   A/C♯   G2   D2/A   D/A   Asus   A   G/B   Em   Dsus

D   A(add4)/C♯   C   Bm   Gmaj7   G   D/F♯   F♯   A(add4)

Grace

Words and Music by
LAURA STORY

Key: E♭

E♭maj7 E♭6 E♭maj7 E♭6

E♭(no3) E♭sus E♭2(no3) E♭ E♭/D
My heart is so proud. My eyes are so unfocused.
Cm7 A♭2 B♭sus E♭
I see the things You do through me as great things I have done.
E♭/G A♭2 E♭ B♭/D Cm7
And now You gently break me, then lovingly You take me
A♭2 E♭/G A♭2 B♭sus B♭
And hold me as my Father and mold me as my Maker.

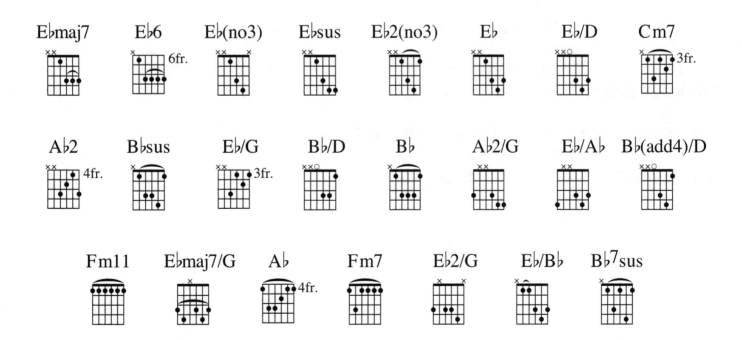

     E♭   **E♭/G**   **A♭2**
I ask You: "How many times will You pick me up,
    B♭sus   **B♭/D**   **E♭**
When I keep on letting You down?
    Cm7   **A♭2**
And each time I will fall short of Your glory,
    A♭2   **B♭sus**
How far will forgiveness abound?"
      E♭/G   **A♭2/G** **E♭/G** **A♭2**
And You answer: "My child,   I love you.
E♭/A♭ **E♭**   **B♭(add4)/D** **Cm7**
And as long as you're seeking My   face,
    Fm11   **B♭sus**   **E♭maj7**
You'll walk in the power of My daily-sufficient grace."

A♭2 **E♭maj7/G** **A♭2** **B♭sus**

   E♭   **A♭2**   **B♭sus**   **E♭** **E♭/D**
At times I may grow weak and feel a bit discouraged,
Cm7   **A♭2**   **B♭sus** **E♭**
Knowing that someone, somewhere could do a better   job.
  E♭/G   **A♭2**   **E♭**   **B♭/D** **Cm7**
For who am I to serve You? I know I don't deserve You.
  Fm11   **E♭/G**   **A♭2**   **B♭sus**
And that's the part that burns in my heart and keeps me hanging on.

A♭ **A♭2** **E♭/G** **A♭2/G** **E♭/G** **Fm7**

   B♭   **E♭**   **E♭2/G** **E♭/G** **A♭**
You are so patient with   me,   Lord.

A♭2 **E♭/G** **A♭2/G** **E♭/G** **B♭sus** **E♭/B♭** **B♭7sus**

A♭2 **E♭maj7/G** **A♭2** **E♭/B♭** **B♭sus** **E♭**

Grace

Words and Music by
LAURA STORY

Key: E♭ (Capo 1: D)

Dmaj7   D6   Dmaj7   D6

   D(no3)   Dsus   D2(no3)   D   D/C♯
My heart is so proud. My eyes are so unfocused.
 Bm7   G2   Asus   D
I see the things You do through me as great things I have done.
   D/F♯   G2   D   A/C♯   Bm7
And now You gently break me, then lovingly You take me
  G2   D/F♯   G2   Asus   A
And hold me as my Father and mold me as my Maker.

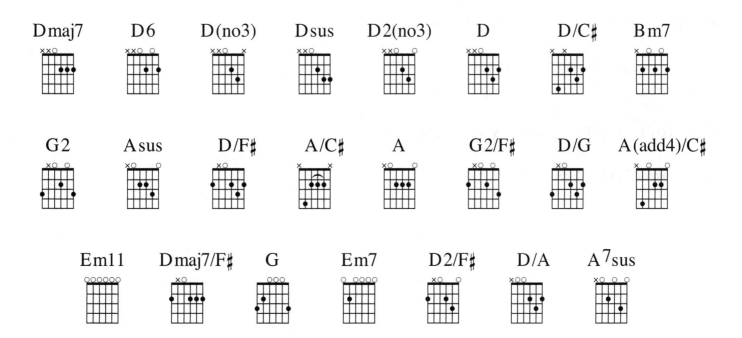

```
       D            D/F♯              G2
I ask You: "How many times will You pick me up,
       Asus      A/C♯         D
When I keep on letting You down?
      Bm7                 G2
And each time I will fall short of Your glory,
      G2                      Asus
How far will forgiveness abound?"
          D/F♯            G2/F♯   D/F♯    G2
And You answer: "My child,          I love you.
D/G    D              A(add4)/C♯  Bm7
And as long as you're seeking  My   face,
       Em11                    Asus          Dmaj7
You'll walk in the power of My daily-sufficient grace."
```

```
G2   Dmaj7/F♯   G2   Asus
```

```
    D                 G2        Asus          D   D/C♯
At times I may grow weak and feel a bit discouraged,
Bm7               G2                         Asus    D
Knowing that someone, somewhere could do a better    job.
    D/F♯          G2            D       A/C♯   Bm7
For who am I to serve You? I know I don't deserve You.
      Em11            D/F♯                  G2                 Asus
And that's the part that burns in my heart and keeps me hanging on.
```

```
G   G2   D/F♯   G2/F♯   D/F♯   Em7
```

```
      A    D     D2/F♯   D/F♯   G
You are so patient with     me,    Lord.
```

```
G2   D/F♯   G2/F♯   D/F♯   Asus   D/A   A7sus
```

```
G2   Dmaj7/F♯   G2   D/A   Asus   D
```

He Will Not Let Go

**Words and Music by
LAURA STORY**

Key: C

C   Am   F   G(add4)   F2/A

    C   Am   F   Dm7
It may take time on this journey slow. What lies ahead, I'm not sure I know.
        C   Am   G   Gsus   F   G7sus   C
But the hand that holds this flailing soul,   He will not let go.

        C   Am9   F2   Dm9
There may be days when I cannot breathe. There may be scars that will stay with me.
        C   G/B   Am9   C2/G   F   G7sus   C   F/A   C
But the deepest stains, they will be washed clean. And He will not let   go.

    F2(♯4)   F   Am11   G
When all around my soul gives way, He then is all my hope and stay.
    F2(♯4)   F   Am9   G(add4)   F   F2
When grief has paralyzed my heart, His grip holds even tighter than the dark.

       C   Am   F   Dm9
I've heard it said this too shall pass, the joy will come, that the hurt won't last.
    C   G/B   Am9   C/G   F   Gsus   G   Am7
So, I will trust that within His grasp I am not   a-   lone,
    F2/A   G/B   C   Am   F   G(add4)   F2/A   G/B   C
For He will not let go.

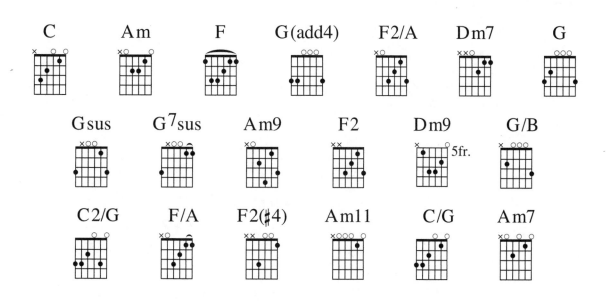